Circle the animals that from Africa

Answers

Asian elephant

Golden lion tamarin

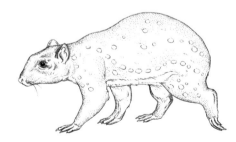

Lowland paca

Finish the octopus

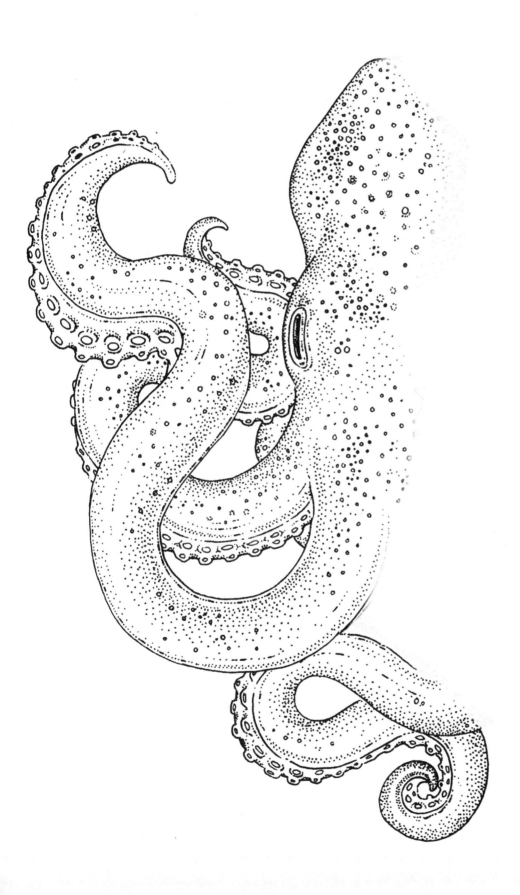

Angel octopus

Velodona togata
Mantle length: 16 centimetres
This deep-sea octopus lives at depths between 200–700 metres.

Add more frogs
to this rainforest habitat

Examples of rainforest frogs

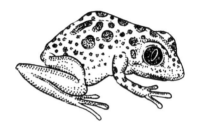

Blue poison-dart frog

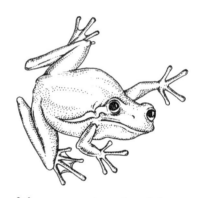

Waxy monkey leaf frog

Granular poison-dart frog

Match the animal pairs

(there are invertebrates, amphibians and birds)

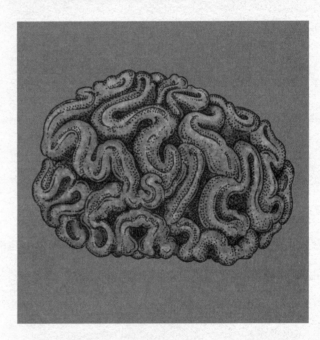
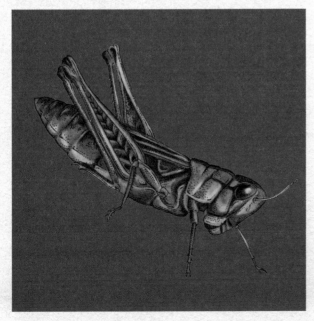

Answers

The brain coral and green grasshopper are both invertebrates

The axolotl and Allen's worm salamander are both amphibians

The bateleur and ruby-topaz hummingbird are both birds

How to draw a lion

1
2
3
4

Try it yourself

Lion

Panthera leo
Length: 2.85 metres
Second only to the tiger in size, this big cat is
immediately recognizable thanks to its mane. It lives in
prides where the females hunt together for food.

Add animals to this coastal habitat

Some coastal habitat creatures

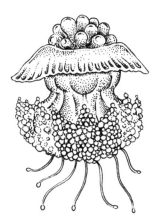

Crown jellyfish

Calico scallop

Cushion star

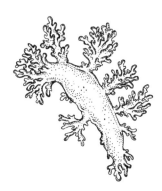

Bushy-backed sea slug

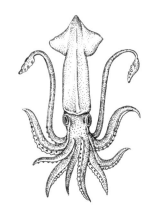

Northern short-fin squid

Label the parts of the fish

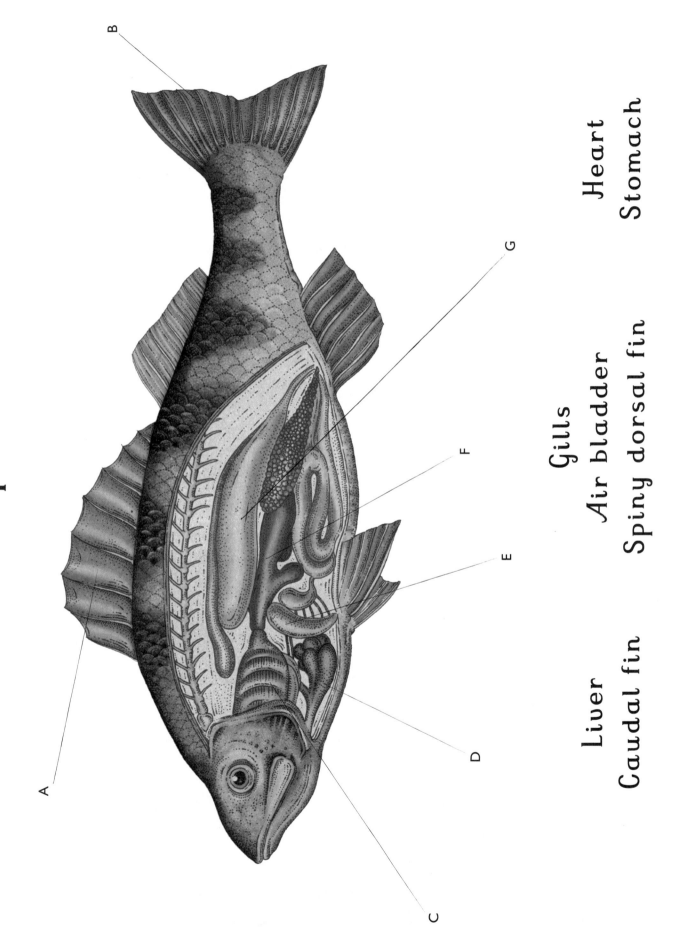

A

B

C

D

E

F

G

Liver   Gills   Heart

Caudal fin   Air bladder   Stomach

               Spiny dorsal fin

Answers

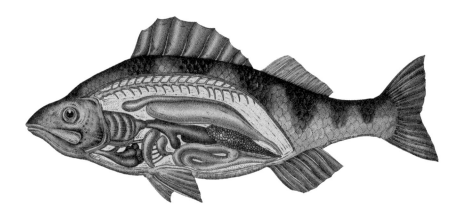

A - Spiny dorsal fin
B - Caudal fin
C - Gills
D - Heart
E - Liver
F - Stomach
G - Air bladder

Circle the matching pair of ornate horned frogs

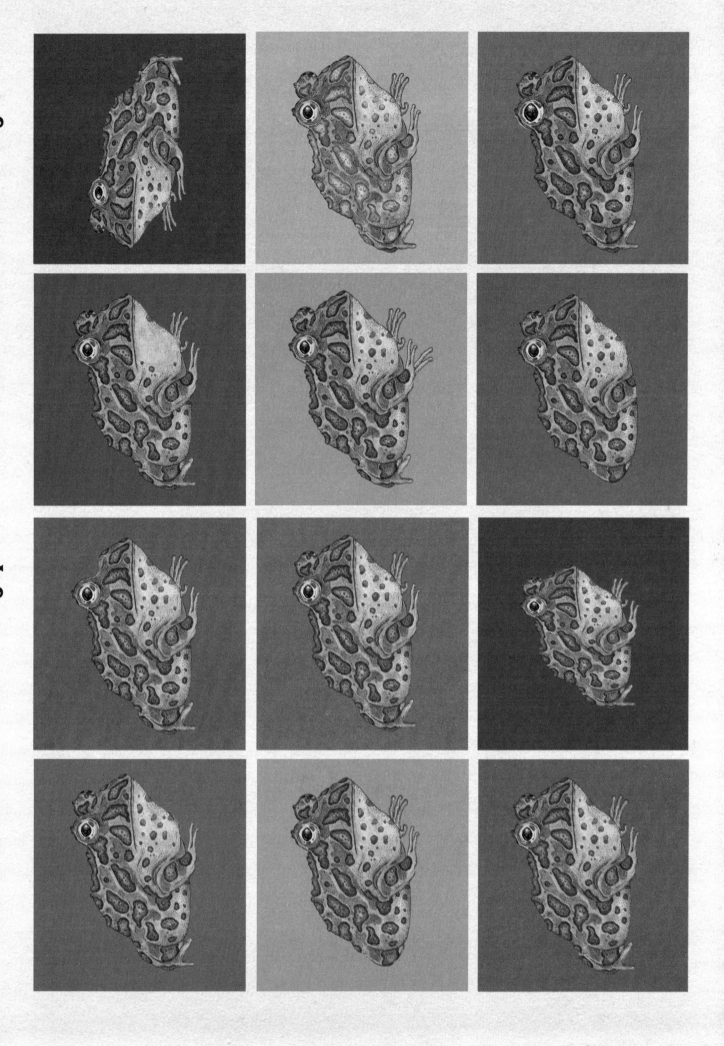

Answer

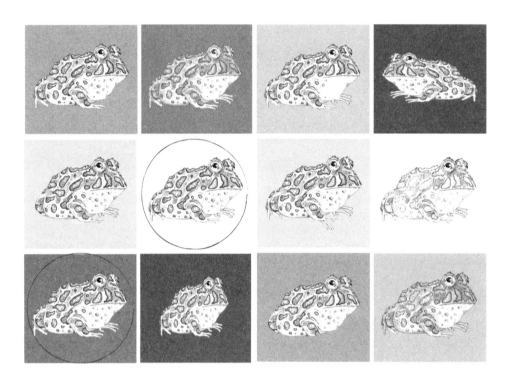

Complete the flying insects

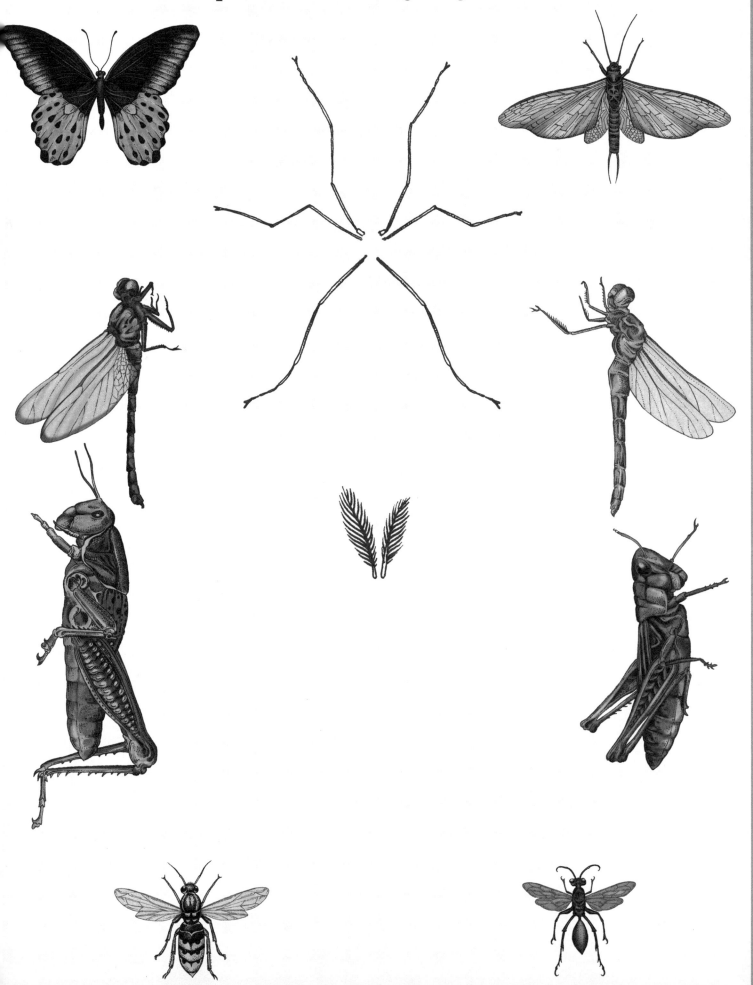

Examples of flying insects

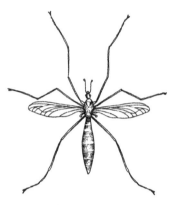

Crane fly

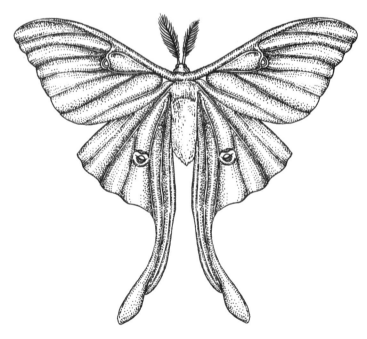

Luna moth

Colour in the
desert scene

Baja California collared lizard

Crotaphytus vestigium
Body length: 9 centimetres
This creature hibernates under a rock in the cold winter months
and becomes active in the warmer seasons. When running, it can
become bipedal, standing up on its two hind legs.

Copy this goliath heron
onto the grid below

Goliath heron

Ardea goliath
Height: 142 centimetres
This is the largest and tallest species of heron on Earth, and is able to
walk in deeper waters than its competition, spearing prey with its sharp
bill. It is commonly found in sub-Saharan Africa.

Put these animals in their true size order, 1 being the smallest and 8 the biggest

Answers

1 - Common wasp – 1.4cm
2 - Granular poison-dart frog – 2cm
3 - Ruby-topaz hummingbird – 8cm
4 - Luna moth – 10cm
5 - Emperor penguin – 1.1m
6 - Green sea turtle – 1.5m
7 - Spotted eagle ray – 1.8m
8 - Humpback whale – 14m

Create your own exotic bird

Exotic birds

Ruby-throated hummingbird

Ruby-topaz hummingbird

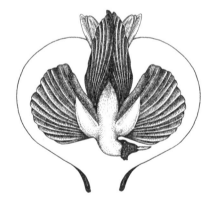

Greater bird-of-paradise

Help the clownfish escape
the jellyfish maze

Answer

Colour the moth and butterfly

Blue Mormon butterfly

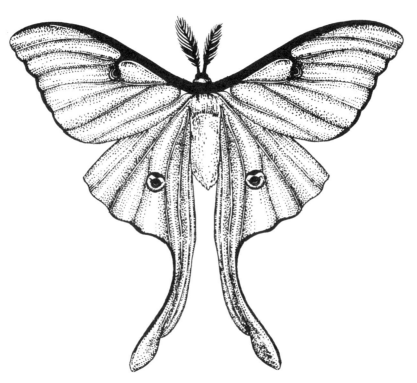

Luna moth

Add some more snakes
to the tangle

Snakes

Snakes are characterised by their lack of limbs and their long, tube-like
bodies. They are believed to have descended from lizards, losing their
limbs in the process of evolution.

Spot the difference

Answers

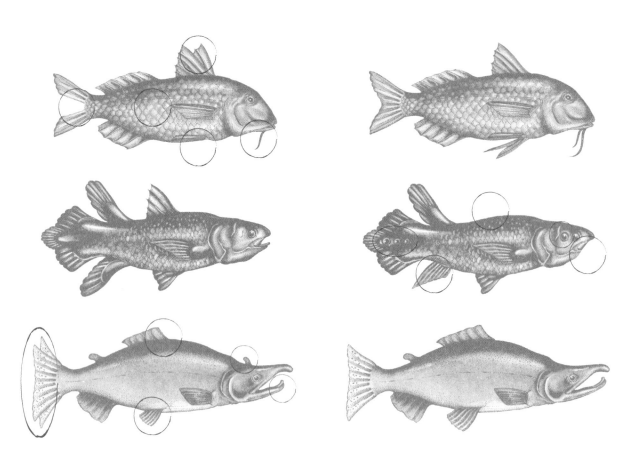

Create your own bat face

 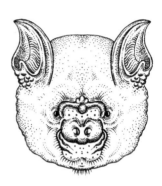

Bats

There are more species of bat than any other type of
mammal, after rodents, with over 900 recognised species.
Bats are the only mammals to have evolved to fly. They
are mostly nocturnal creatures, sleeping through the day
and coming out to hunt at twilight.

Label the crocodile skeleton

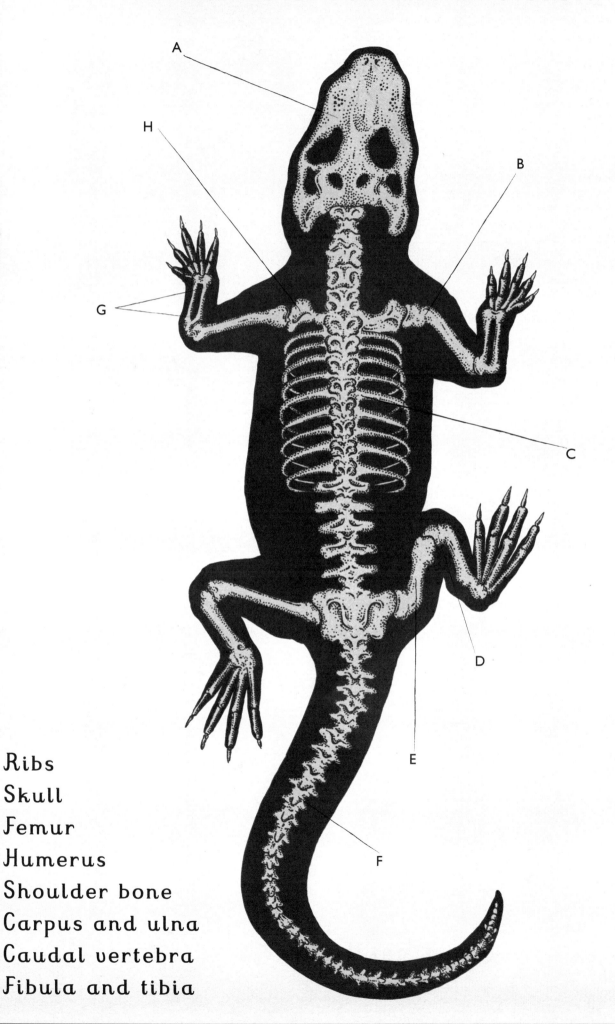

A

H

B

G

C

D

E

F

Ribs
Skull
Femur
Humerus
Shoulder bone
Carpus and ulna
Caudal vertebra
Fibula and tibia

Answers

A - Skull
B - Humerus
C - Ribs
D - Fibula and tibia
E - Femur
F - Caudal vertebra
G - Carpus and ulna
H - Shoulder bone

Add an emperor penguin chick

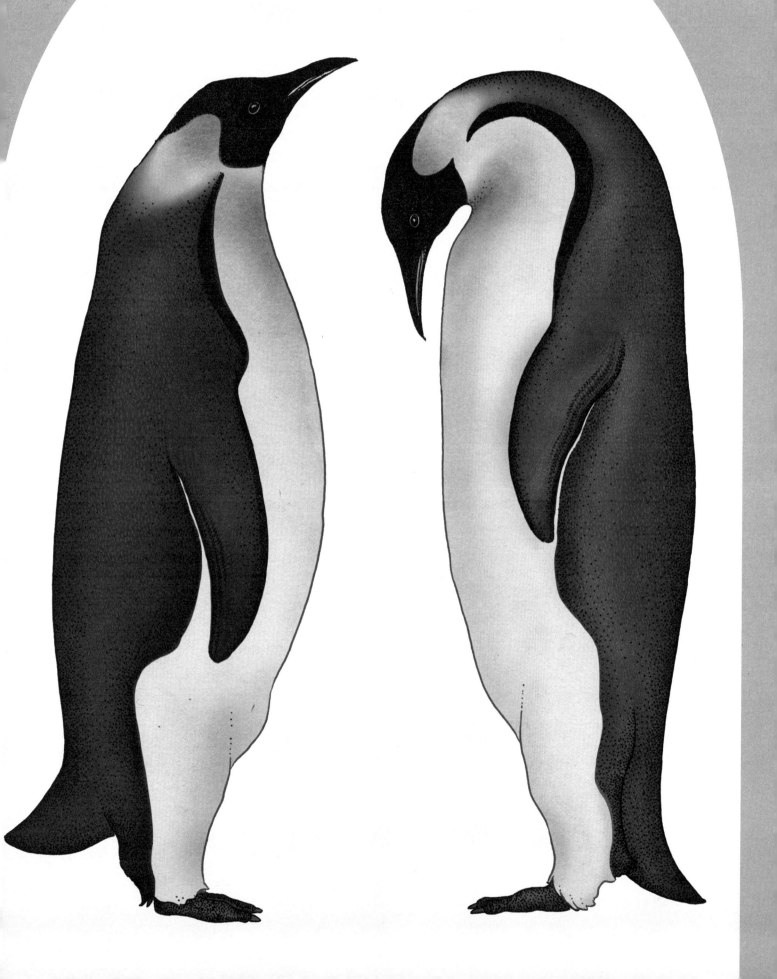

Emperor penguin

Aptenodytes forsteri
Height: 1.1 metres
The emperor penguin is famous for its
reproductive cycle. It chooses to breed during
the Antarctic winter between May and June, when
no other creature inhabits the region, thus
reducing the threat of predators.

Add wings to these insects

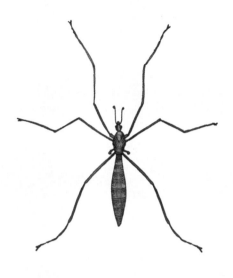

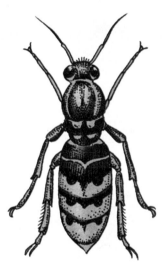

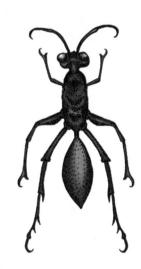

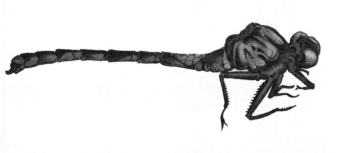

Insects with wings

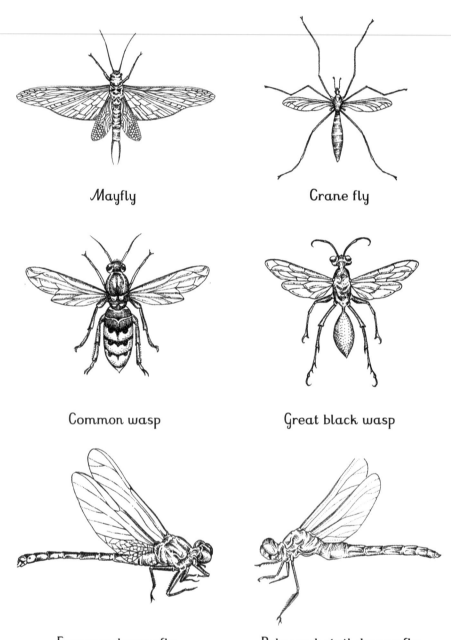

Mayfly

Crane fly

Common wasp

Great black wasp

Emperor dragonfly

Pale snaketail dragonfly

Draw the crested caracara

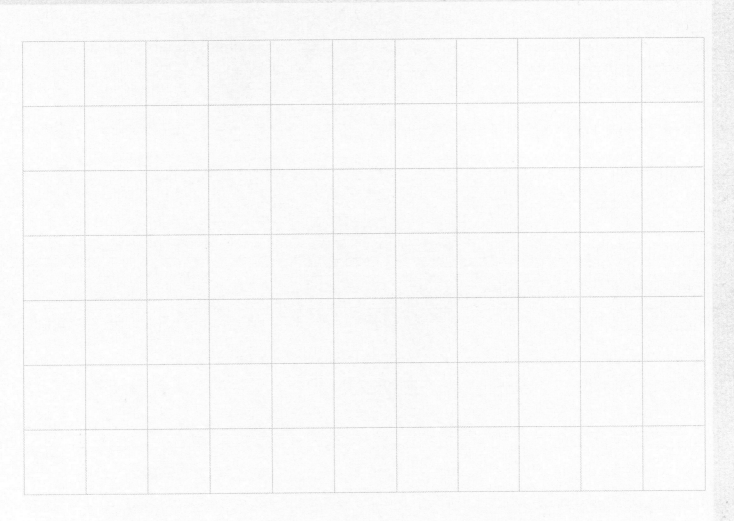

Crested caracara

Crested caracara

Caracara plancus
Wingspan: 1.2 metres
The crested caracara is found in open land from the
southern parts of North America down to Peru and
Amazonian Brazil, and is a common sight on cattle ranches. It
is not an agile flyer and seldom hunts for prey, opting instead
to scavenge for food and feed on carrion.

Circle the predators

Answers

Lion

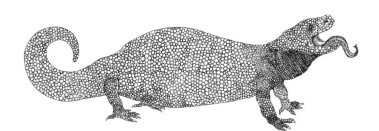

Gila monster

White's treefrog

This pattern is from a terrapin shell. Fill the page by repeating the pattern

Diamondback terrapin

Malaclemys terrapin
Length: 15 centimetres
The mild-mannered diamondback terrapin lives in brackish
lagoons, tidal marshlands and sandy beaches in east-coast
America. The species nearly became extinct due to over-
hunting and destruction of its habitat.

Spot the
marsupials

Answers

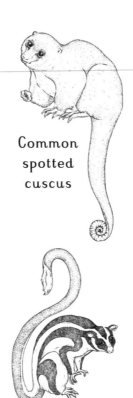

Common
spotted
cuscus

Striped possum

Sugar glider

Koala

Draw your own food chain

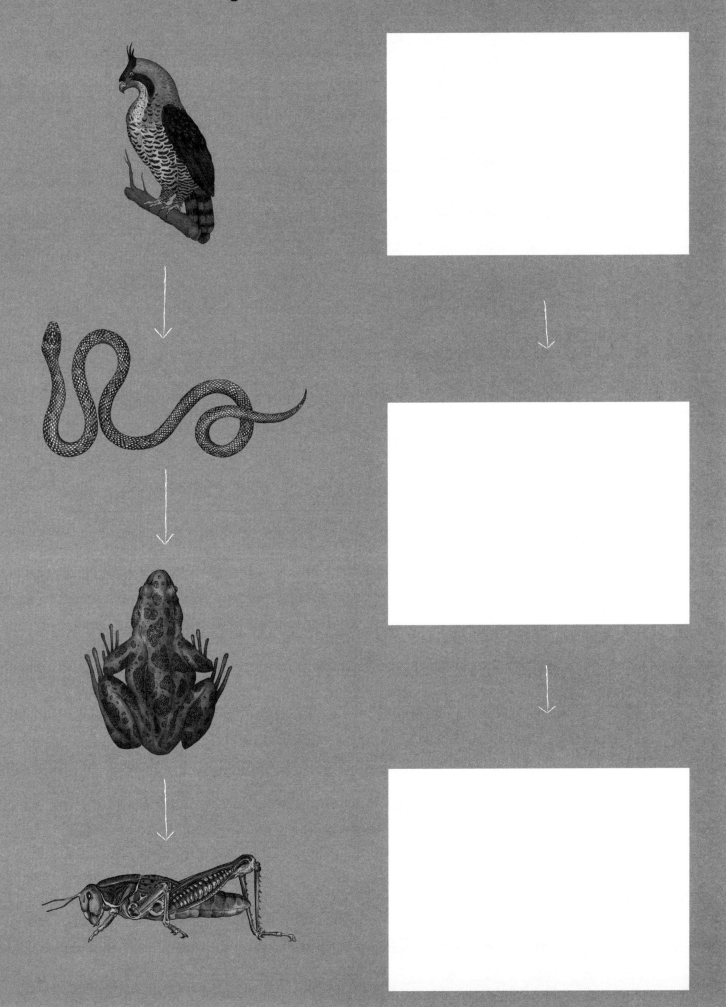

Another example of a food chain

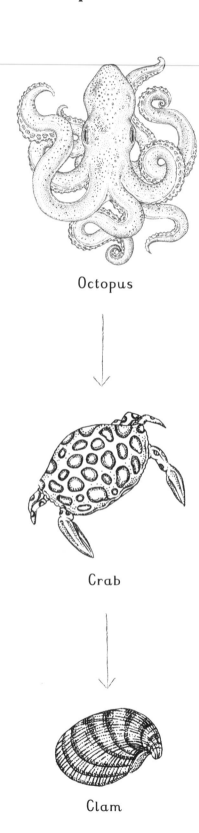

Octopus

Crab

Clam

Finish the sea creatures

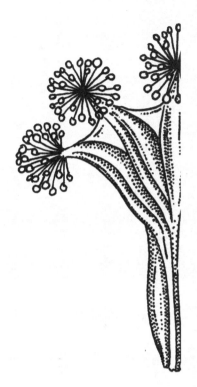

Sea creatures

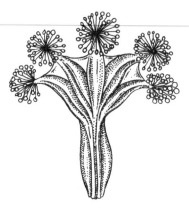

Stalked jellyfish

Blue button jellyfish

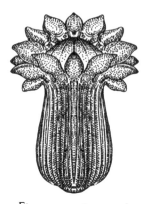

Flowerpot coral

Add fish to
this coral reef

Examples of some coral reef fish

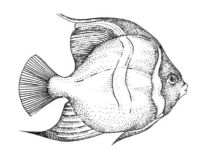

French angelfish

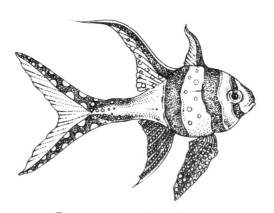

Banggai cardinalfish

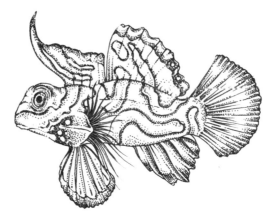

Mandarinfish

Colour the sea sponges

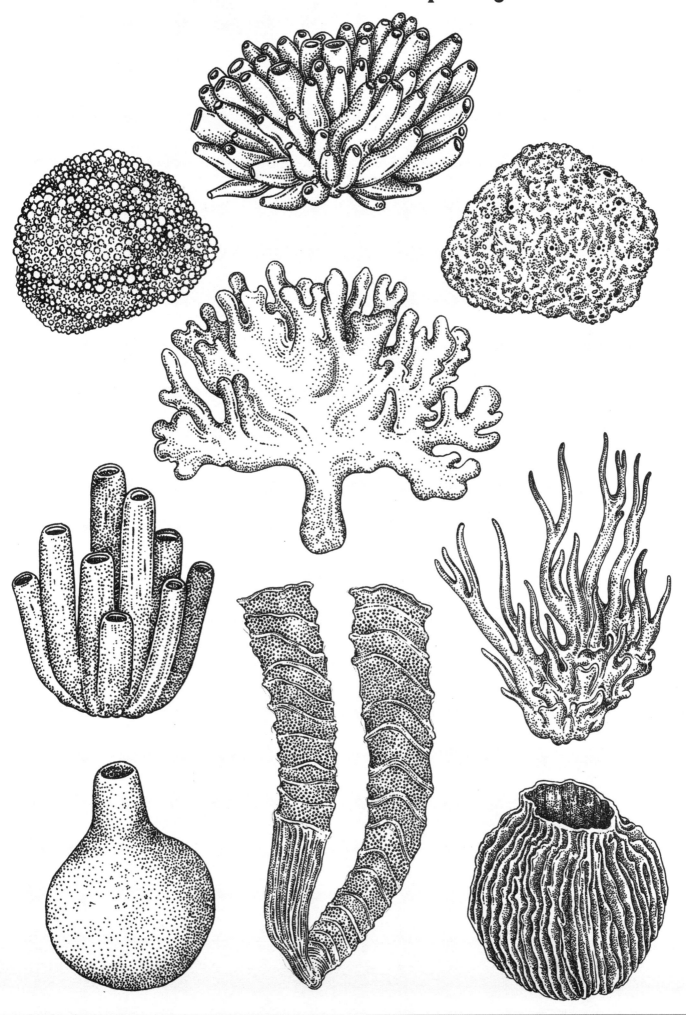

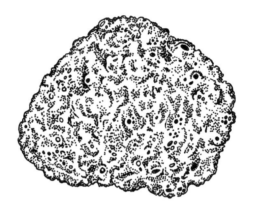

Sea sponges

Porifera, or sponges, date back to 665 million years ago. The evolution of the multicellular sponge was one of the most significant developments in natural history. Living exclusively underwater, sponges can be found in all habitats, from tropical seas to icy waters.

Fill in the giraffe's spots

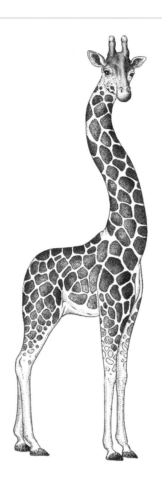

Masai giraffe

Giraffa camelopardalis tippelskirchi
Height: 5.5 metres
The African Masai giraffe is the tallest land mammal on Earth.
Its long legs and neck have evolved to allow it to feed from the
treetops, and its long and flexible tongue extends to gather in
twigs and leaves. When competing for a mate, males duel by
battering one another with their long necks.

Draw the ray

Thornback ray

Thornback ray

Raja clavata
Length: 85 centimetres
This kite-shaped ray is one of the most commonly seen species, although
identification can be difficult because colouration varies wildly from
fish to fish. It has between 36 and 44 rows of teeth in its upper jaw, and its
long, solid tail has thorns running down its length.

Spot the difference

Answers

How to draw an elephant

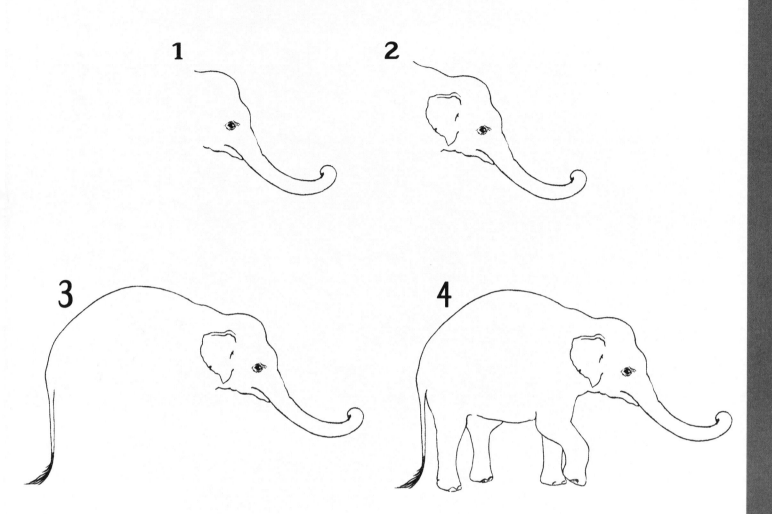

1 2 3 4

Try it yourself

Asian elephant

Elephas maxiumus
Height: 2.6 metres
The Asian elephant has smaller ears, smaller tusks - if it has
any at all - and a back more arched than its African cousin's.
Elephants are instantly recognisable thanks to their unique
and flexible trunks, which they use to grab and hold objects
with, and their large, flat ears.

Match the animal pairs

(there are amphibians, mammals and reptiles)

Answers

The White's treefrog and Mandarin salamander are both amphibians

The De Brazza's monkey and Weddell
seal are both mammals

The Gila monster and Indian star tortoise are both reptiles

Fill in the missing stages of these frog and moth life cycles

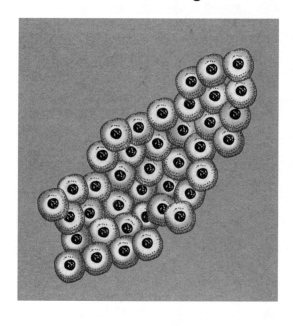

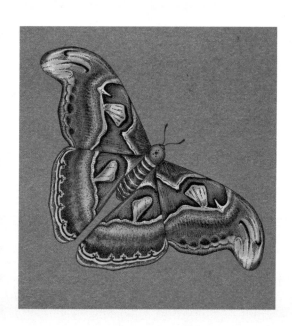

Answers

Frogspawn

Eggs

Tadpole

Chrysalis

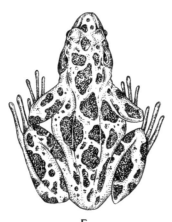

Frog

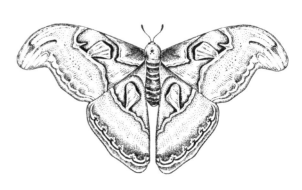

Moth

Complete the animals

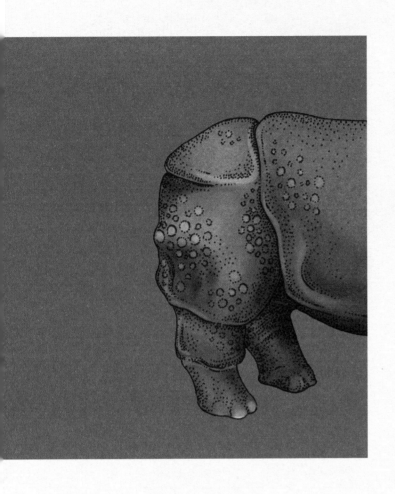

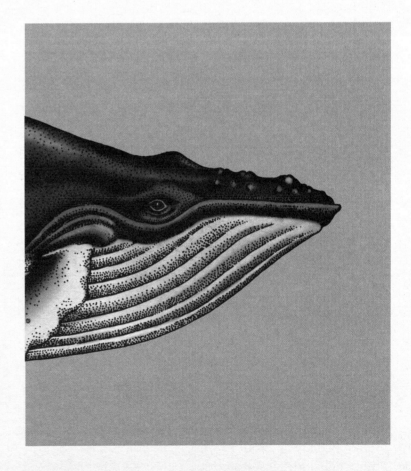

Completed animals

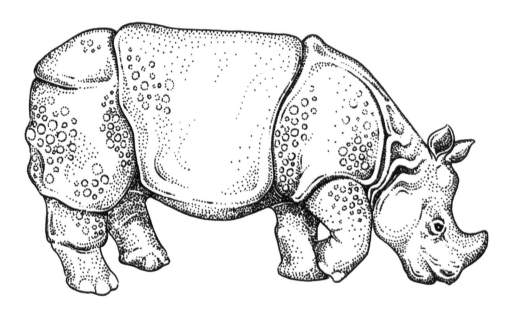

Indian rhinoceros

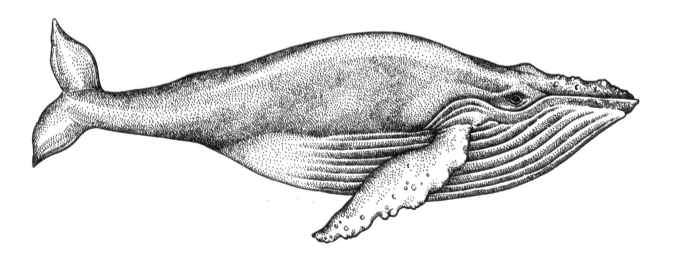

Humpback whale